For Susan
May our paths
keep crossing
Good luck on
your journey
Angela

Once in a Blue Moon

Angela Stoner

illustrations Michèle Wright

fal

fal

First edition 2005

Copyright   – text Angela Stoner
                – illustrations Michèle Wright

ISBN 0-9544980-4-6

Cover design - Michèle Wright

Published by

fal publications
PO Box 74
Truro
TR1 1XS

www.falpublications.co.uk

Printed by R Booth Ltd Antron Hill, Mabe, Cornwall

The Mermaid's Tale

If you visit Cornwall and go far west to the very end of the land, you may find yourself stirred by wildness and magic. Even the place-names, Porthgwarra, Gwithian and Morvah are mysterious and other-worldly. It is easy, staring out at a fairy-tale castle on an island surrounded by mist, to believe in mermaids and to hear them singing. Zennor, Godrevy and Lamorna are just some of the many places where mermaids have been seen.

It is very rare for mermaids to venture near land, even to shores as magical as Cornwall, so you will probably never see one. Most mermaids live far out in the ocean well away from the dry world of humans. They live deep under the sea, deeper than our deepest dreams, out in the wildest part of the sea, beyond our wildest imagination.

In this part of the ocean, the sun scarcely penetrates. Mermaids and dolphins live by the iridescence of mother-of-pearl and the fluorescence of electric fish.

It is a deep, dark, dangerous world.

But in spite of this their world is beautiful. There are palaces of deep indigo, purple, coral and ivory. There are huge caverns carved from mother-of-pearl in which gorgeous fish swim and where purple and green sea plants float and eddy.

Here, mermaids play. They dance, swim and glide with a sinuous breath-taking grace. If you could see them moving, you would think they were flying.

They do not speak to each other, but they sing! And what songs! It would fill your heart to bursting to hear their trills, their crescendos, their harmonies, their pure, sweet lilting melodies!

But one mermaid always felt alone - though she did not know why.

While the other mermaids were content to sing, swim and play, she dreamed of a world of bright, dry, dazzling colours.

She sang of this dream to other mermaids, but they didn't understand and, as she sang, she thought nobody was listening.

But somehow her song made its way to the top of the world. The mermaid did not know this, nor even that this dry world she had dreamed about really existed. She simply sang.

As soon as she had finished her song, sadness overwhelmed her and though legend has it that they cannot do such things, the mermaid began to cry. As her salt tears mingled with the waves, she noticed a strange pattern, made by a pale golden, watery light.

This light had come from our sun, though she had no way of knowing this. In the depths where they live, this phenomenon is so rare that mermaids have no word, or more accurately no tone, for such a thing but it pierced her heart with joy.

Then she heard a sound she did recognise – but only from strange, less than half-believed legends. It was the cry of a human.

They say mermaids have no souls, but either this is a lie or else the song of the fisherman called her soul into being. Whatever the explanation, the fact is her soul leaped. She listened to that song as it echoed throughout the sea, all the way from the surface and she knew it to be the sigh of a human!

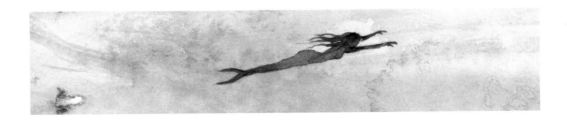

She could have swum up to the surface there and then, to sing to him her deepest song of seduction, so he would immediately plunge in after her. But she knew that if she did so, the fisherman would probably die and she would have only a corpse, not a brave young man, in her arms.

Or, she could visit the wise woman and arrange to lose her voice and tail so she could live with the man. But what was the point in that? Her tail was her power, and her voice, her very life. And all the stories said that if she lost her tail and walked on land, every step would cut her feet like knives.

But as she listened to that sigh, it seemed she knew at once what the human needed. She would not be able to live with him. Instead, she would search the very deepest, darkest part of the ocean, to find the moonstone that she knew the fisherman secretly craved.

She dived deep. She plunged into the dark. She dived with courage, even though she feared the dreadful creatures in the ocean's depths.

She plunged deeper and deeper, down to where there was no air and no light. Her gills began to give up, her powerful tail to tire, and her eyes to fail.

In the deep dark she lay, stiller than still.

After a long while, she began to see the moon's reflection and, hidden among the sea forest, the moon-stone.

But dare she dive so far? It was so deep, far below where she had already dived.

But dive she did, sustained by her sacred dream.

She slept, dreamed. Her moonstone grew bluer and brighter. She woke from her deep sleep. She would never be able to dance with the fisherman, nor he to swim with her but she could give him what he most craved. She began to swim towards the surface.

She sang a song of joy all the way, even though she was tired to the bone from her diving. As the blue moon rose, she heard the fisherman's boat gliding towards her.

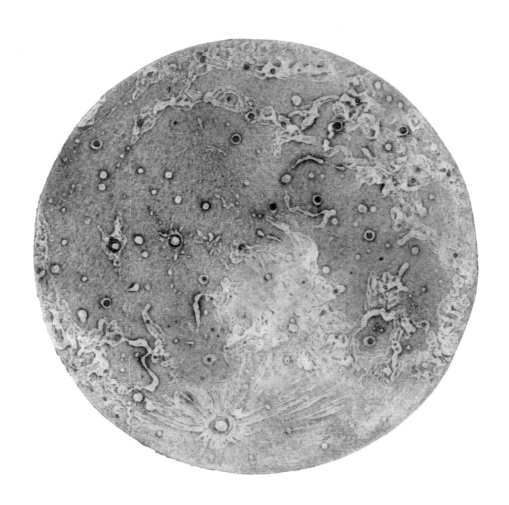

She broke the surface and began to use her pitiful little lungs to sing to the fisherman and guide him to her.

As the boat sailed towards her she held the moonstone up to him, although her arms ached. She sang to him, although she thought her lungs would burst.

And she reached up to give him the moonstone …

only to find that she was reaching up to receive the beautiful golden sunstone she had never known her heart craved, and then...

Once in a Blue Moon

Angela Stoner

illustrations Michèle Wright

fal

Thank you to my husband John and my son Leon for always believing in me.

For Thomas and all my nieces and nephews – may you always follow your dreams and listen to your deepest wisdom.

Angela

For two little girls – Kira Lomas, often my inspiration, and waterbabe, Lia Wright.

Thank you to my husband, John David Wright, and Vicky Banner for their patience with me.

Michèle

The Fisherman's Tale

It is difficult to be in Cornwall without feeling a pull from something wild and beyond the every-day. The Cornish people are full of courage, wresting a living from the rocks or the wild seas. Mystery and magic survive in its wells, its quoits and its carns. And around its coast, the sea sings constantly.

Many fishermen ply their trade from the rocky coves of Cornwall. This story is about one of these, who lived in St Ives and whose heart was full of strange dreams.

He had a great talent for fishing, as if Neptune himself guided him to where the fish swam and his net was always full. He never went hungry and had carefully accrued great savings.

Yet it seemed to him as if his heart were always empty. He fished alone, feeling as though the wild were calling to him and that only the deepest seas could fulfil his dreams.

He dare not speak of what stirred his soul, for fear of ridicule, but restlessly sailed the seven seas and chased adventures in search of he knew not what!

One night, he sailed far out to sea, stared up at the moon and sobbed.

"Oh, let me have my dream!" he wailed, "even if I do not know what it is!" He fell asleep, and dreamed of the strangest fish he had ever seen, of iridescent palaces, of coral and gently swaying sea forests.

He was woken by a deep, golden light and a beautiful song that pierced him to the marrow.

He knew that song! It was a mermaid's song. You might expect that he would dive straight after that song to be with the beautiful mermaid.

But only a foolish fisherman would have done such a thing, for it would lead to certain death in the arms of a cold siren. He was a wise fisherman, so he did not do that.

You might expect he would try to lure the mermaid to his boat, so that he could have her as a wife and companion. But only a foolish fisherman would do such a thing, because were the mermaid to lose her powerful tail and beautiful voice, she would lose her very essence. He was a wise fisherman, so he did not do that.

You might expect that he would tie himself to his mast and stop his ears and sail back to shore. He could have pretended he'd never heard her song, and gone back to his ordinary life. That may seem very sensible, but the wisdom of this fisherman knew otherwise, so he did not do that either.

He was, as I have said before, a wise fisherman, an exceptionally wise fisherman. He was also brave and generous, so he lay still in the boat and asked the oldest and deepest and wisest part of him what her song might mean.

And when he knew, he lay and listened to her song, and sang back to her and knew what he must do.

He sailed back to shore, knowing what the mermaid craved, even though she didn't know herself. He would fashion for her a beautiful statue of gold – or "sunstone" as she would call it.

Tears fell down his face as he worked. The gold had cost him the price of many catches and taken all his carefully accrued savings.

He knew that he would give the golden sunstone to her freely and gladly, even though he could never dance with her. Her great beauty had haunted his dreams, but he knew that he could never enjoy this beauty for himself.

By day and night he worked, blistering his hands. Not only on the beautiful carving for the mermaid, but also on building the boat which would carry him safely far out to sea where she lived.

Plank by weathered plank, he built the boat, nail by tempered nail, he hammered and shaped it true. He forged the special rudder that would keep him on course with ruthless diligence.

He put on special clothing, for he knew he must be protected from the elements. When the blue moon was new, he set sail. He was guided by the stars, knowing that each one shone with secret dreams he hardly dared name.

He sailed day and night, although his fingers were blistered from his hard work and his bones ached and cried out for rest. He ignored the many shoals of fish he passed although he was hungry and impoverished by buying the gold for the mermaid.

The fisherman's journey took him far out to the wildest, darkest part of the ocean. He was afraid, but the gold of the carving he had made seemed to warm his heart, and his rudder and the stars would show him the way. But now that he was in the middle of the ocean, cloud came over the stars, and the rudder failed. He was lost, alone and adrift, with only his dream to sustain him.

Now, even through his special protective clothing, he began to feel the cold, which cut through to his marrow, and seemed to freeze his soul.

At last the blue moon rose and with it came the barely audible notes of the mermaid's call.

He responded with a great and powerful song of his own, and sailed his boat towards her. As she broke the surface, he saw her for the first time. He leaned over to give the mermaid her beautiful golden carving...

only to find that he was reaching down to receive the beautiful blue
moonstone he had not known his heart craved, and then…

the mermaid grew legs and, as she danced, her feet did not cut like knives but felt pleasure as she danced and sang more sweetly than she ever had........

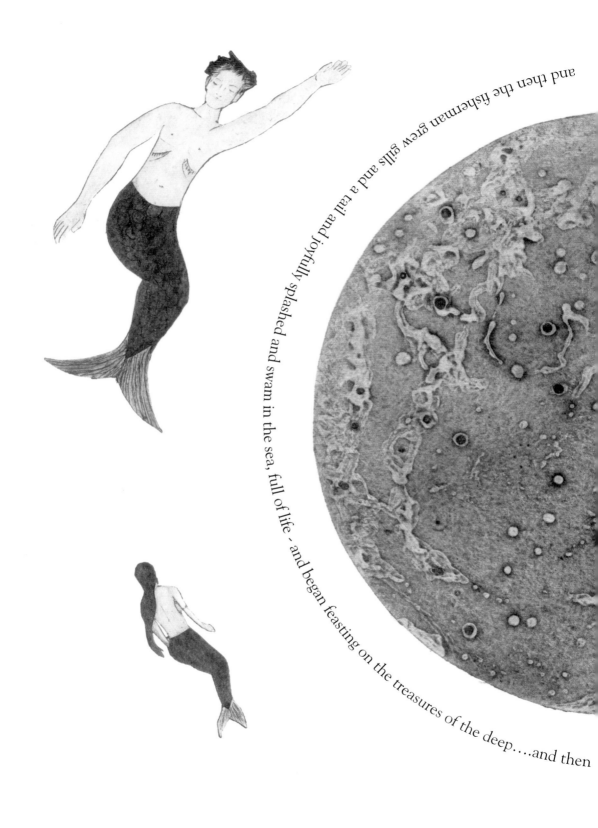

and then the fisherman grew gills and a tail and joyfully splashed and swam in the sea, full of life - and began feasting on the treasures of the deep….and then